A Collection of Wonderful Stories
for 6 year old Boys:

I am a 6 year old super boy

(Inspirational Gift Books for Kids)

Table of Contents

Introduction

Dear boy,

Welcome to a magical journey filled with excitement, adventures, and big dreams! This book is a special collection of wonderful stories crafted just for you, to

inspire your heart and spark your imagination.

As you dive into these pages, you'll find tales of courage and inner strength—stories that show how even the youngest among us can do amazing things. These characters, much like yourself, have big dreams and the determination to reach for the stars.

Remember, no dream is too big, and no challenge is too great. With a brave heart and a strong spirit, you can overcome anything and achieve your greatest desires. These stories are here to remind you of the incredible power you hold within and the endless possibilities that lie ahead.

So, dear boy, get ready to embark on adventures, learn valuable lessons, and discover the fantastic world that awaits you.

Open your heart, let your imagination soar, and enjoy every moment of this exciting journey!

With joy and excitement,
Lili M. Green

Chapter 1.
The Power of Imagination and Dreaming Big

Leo, a bright and cheerful six-year-old, lived in a cozy house filled with laughter and love. His parents, Mr. and Mrs. Johnson, always encouraged him to use his

imagination and believe in the magic of dreams.

One evening, after a day filled with laughter and play, Leo retreated to his small blue room, surrounded by toy planes, action figures, and a carpet that looked like a vast ocean. Above him hung a poster of a large floating island amidst the clouds. Leo would stare at that island every night before falling asleep, wondering what mysteries it held.

Just as Leo's eyelids were getting heavy, the poster began to give off a soft glow. The floating island started to move, and a gentle voice whispered, "Dream big, Leo. Come aboard!"

Suddenly, Leo found himself standing at the edge of the floating island, feeling the soft grass beneath his feet and the cool

breeze brushing against his face. The island was magnificent, with tall trees, sparkling waterfalls, and animals he'd never seen before.

A kind-looking creature with feathers on its head approached him. "Hello, Leo. I am Flyn, the guardian of this island. We've been waiting for you."

"Me? Why?" asked Leo, surprised.

Flyn smiled. "This island is a place for dreamers like you, and we need a captain. We've heard of your great imagination, and we believe you're the one who can help us reach new skies and discover unknown lands."

Leo's eyes widened. "But I'm just a little boy. How can I be a captain?"

6

Flyn gently tapped Leo's heart. "It's not the size that matters, but the strength of your dreams and imagination. Do you think you can do it?"

Leo gave a determined nod. "I'll try my best!"

Over the next few days, Leo learned the ways of the island. He communicated with the animals, learned to steer the island using a giant compass, and discovered hidden treasures. Every challenge he faced, he overcame with the power of his imagination.

One day, dark clouds began to gather. A storm was approaching, and the island was in danger. The creatures looked worried, but Leo stood tall. He closed his eyes and remembered all the stories he had imagined

in his room. Harnessing the power of those dreams, he imagined a protective shield around the island.

As the storm raged, the shield glowed, keeping everyone safe. When the storm finally passed, the island was untouched, and the creatures cheered for Captain Leo.

Flyn approached him with a twinkle in his eyes. "See, Leo? You have the power to turn your dreams into reality. Never forget that."

Leo woke up the next morning, back in his blue room, with the sun streaming through the window. The poster of the floating island still hung on the wall, but now it held a special place in his heart. He realized that with a strong imagination and big dreams, he could overcome any challenge.

A few weeks later, something magical happened! The local community center announced a drawing competition for kids, with the theme "Dreams and Adventures." Leo spent days sketching, coloring, and bringing his imagination to life on paper. With every stroke of his crayon, he remembered his adventure on the floating island and the lessons he had learned.

Finally, the day of the competition arrived and Leo submitted his artwork: a vibrant and detailed depiction of the floating island, complete with the tall trees, sparkling waterfalls, and the kind creature Flyn.

The judges were amazed by the creativity and imagination of this young boy. His artwork stood out among the rest, capturing the essence of dreaming.

Leo won the first prize! And he suddenly realized that his adventure on the floating island, though a dream, had given him the courage to share his imagination with the world. His dream had indeed come true, not just on the canvas of his drawing, but in the belief he had in himself and the support he received from his family.

With a heart full of gratitude and eyes sparkling with confidence, Leo understood that the power of imagination and dreaming big could turn even the wildest dreams into reality.

Chapter 2.
Toys and Adventures

In a little town named Green Meadows, there was a boy named Max. He had a toy soldier he called Sir Brave, and the two were inseparable. They went on countless adventures together, from battling dragons

in the living room to discovering hidden treasures in the backyard.

One sunny morning, Max couldn't find Sir Brave. He searched high and low: under the bed, behind the couch, and even inside his shoe! But Sir Brave was nowhere to be found. Max felt a knot in his stomach. How could he have adventures without his brave companion?

Just when Max was about to give up, a soft whisper came from the window. "Looking for someone?" A little bluebird, perched on the windowsill, tilted its head, looking at Max with sparkling eyes.

Max nodded. "Yes, I can't find Sir Brave, my toy soldier. Have you seen him?"

The bluebird fluttered its wings. "Ah, Sir Brave! He's embarked on a grand adventure

in the Enchanted Forest. He's proving his bravery by finding the Golden Feather to bring back to you. But he might need some help."

Max's eyes widened. An adventure in the Enchanted Forest? This was no ordinary task. Only the bravest of the brave ventured there. But he remembered all the times Sir Brave had been by his side during their playtime adventures, and he knew he had to help.

With the bluebird as his guide, Max entered the Enchanted Forest. They crossed bubbling brooks, climbed tall, mossy rocks, and tiptoed past sleeping giants. Along the way, Max learned to trust his instincts, listen to the world around him, and most importantly, believe in himself.

Finally, they reached the heart of the forest where they found Sir Brave, standing tall and determined at the base of a golden tree. But guarding the tree was a mischievous squirrel, chattering and hopping around.

Sir Brave said in his tiny voice, "Max! I've been trying to get the Golden Feather, but this squirrel won't let me!"

Max knelt down and addressed the squirrel. "Hello! Sir Brave needs the feather to prove his bravery. Can we please have one?"

The squirrel looked at Max, then at Sir Brave, and finally nodded. "Only if you promise to always take care of each other and always find ways to have adventures together."

Max smiled. "Promise!"

The squirrel handed over a shimmering Golden Feather to Sir Brave, and together with Max and the bluebird, they journeyed back home.

Returning to his room, Max placed Sir Brave on his special shelf, right next to the sparkling Golden Feather. He realized that real adventures came from facing challenges with courage and having friends by your side.

From that day on, Max and Sir Brave had even more adventures, but they also knew the importance of care, friendship, and believing in oneself. This proved to be an important lesson for Max and his other friends. You see, there was a school field trip to the nearby forest park and Max noticed his class mate, Jake, looking hesitant. Max wanted to help.

"What is it, Jake?" Max asked.

"I want to explore the forest, but I'm worried there might be bears in there."

Max thought about his own adventures. Remembering the bravery he and Sir Brave had mustered, Max said, "Jake, every adventure is a chance to discover something new. I've got your back."

That gave Jake the courage he needed. At the forest park, with Max by his side, Jake faced his fears and even found a unique, bird-shaped leaf which became a symbol of their real-life adventure.

Back home, Max realized adventures weren't just about going to far-off places or facing big challenges; it was about finding courage and helping friends find theirs.

16

Chapter 3.
The Silent Musician

Once upon a time, in a town not too far away, there was a little boy named Ethan. Ethan was different from other kids; he was hard of hearing. This meant sounds and voices were softer to him, like whispers from a faraway land.

Ethan had a big secret—he loved music. Now, you might wonder, how could someone who couldn't hear properly love music? But Ethan had his ways.

Every time he walked past the town's music store, he would place his hand on the window and feel the vibrations of the music playing inside. To him, it felt like tiny tickles running up his arm. And he loved it!

One day, as he was passing by the store, Ethan felt a stronger vibration, like a gentle thud-thud-thud. Curious, he went inside and saw a beautiful drum set. The beats from the drum felt like a friendly giant's heartbeat. They were strong and clear.

With a twinkle in his eyes, Ethan thought, "Maybe I can't hear the music like everyone else, but I can feel it!" And that's how Ethan's journey with the drums began.

His parents bought him a drum set, and every day after school, he would sit by it, tapping and drumming, feeling the rhythm flowing through him. He learned to play by feeling the vibrations, the ups and downs, the softs and louds.

Ethan's friend, Mia, would come over and play the guitar while he drummed. Even though Ethan couldn't hear Mia's guitar perfectly, he could feel the rhythm and match his drumming to it. Together, they made beautiful music.

One sunny afternoon, the town decided to host a big community picnic in the park.

There were games, laughter, and lots of delicious food. But the highlight of the day was supposed to be the band performing live music.

Ethan was excited about the picnic, especially because he knew there would be music. With his drums in tow, he headed to the park with his parents.

As the band started playing, Ethan placed his hands on his drums, feeling the vibrations of the music in the air. He closed his eyes and let the rhythm flow through him, matching the beats with his drums.

People around started noticing Ethan. They saw the little boy with the drum set, playing with so much joy and passion, even though he couldn't hear the music like everyone else.

A man from the crowd approached Ethan's parents. "Your son, he's got a real talent. His rhythm is spot on! Has he ever thought of joining a band?"

Ethan's parents were proud and surprised. They knew Ethan loved to play, but they hadn't realized others would appreciate his music too.

Word spread through the picnic, and soon, a small crowd gathered around Ethan, cheering him on. Ethan felt the vibrations of their claps and cheers, fueling his passion for drumming even more.

Mia joined in with her guitar, creating a beautiful harmony. They didn't need a stage or a big audience; the park and the people around them were perfect.

Ethan taught everyone a valuable lesson that day. It's not always about what you can't do but about what you can do. He showed that if you have passion and love for something, you'll always find a way to make it happen, no matter what.

Chapter 4.
The Magic Toy Box

In the bustling town of Brightville, where kids played in parks and laughter echoed in the air, lived a boy named Alex. Alex had a special toy box, painted in royal blue and covered with shiny golden stars. Inside this

box were toys he had collected over the years. There were robots, action figures, puzzles, and even a tiny toy dragon that flapped its wings.

One evening, as Alex was reorganizing his toys, he heard a soft sobbing from outside. Peeping through his window, he saw a new boy sitting alone on a bench. His name was Ben, and he had just moved to Brightville. Ben looked sad and lonely, clutching a teddy bear that had seen better days.

An idea popped into Alex's head. He went to his magic toy box and picked out a toy spaceship that lit up and made zooming sounds. With a determined heart, he walked over to Ben.

"Hi, I'm Alex. I thought you might like this," Alex said, offering the spaceship to Ben.

Ben's eyes widened in amazement. "For me?" he whispered.

Alex nodded. "Every kid in Brightville should have a toy that makes them smile."

From that day on, the magic toy box wasn't just Alex's; it was for every kid in Brightville who needed a smile. Every week, Alex would give away a toy to someone new in town or to someone who was feeling down.

The more toys Alex gave away, the more magical his toy box became. Every time it seemed empty, a new toy would magically appear inside, waiting to be given to a child in need.

News of Alex's kindness spread like wildfire. Inspired by him, other kids started sharing their toys, books, and games.

Brightville's parks were filled with laughter and the sounds of shared stories and games.

One day, as Alex was playing in the park, Ben approached him with a shiny toy robot. "I want to add this to the magic toy box," Ben said with a big smile. "So another kid can feel as happy as I did."

Alex hugged his friend. "The magic isn't in the toy box," he whispered. "It's in our hearts."

Chapter 5.
Night at the Museum

In a bustling town where everyone was always busy, there was a boy named John with a big imagination. John loved stories, especially those about brave heroes, hidden treasures, and far-off lands.

One evening, John's parents had exciting news. "We won a special ticket," his mom exclaimed, "for a night at the museum, just for our family!"

John's heart raced. He'd always dreamed of exploring the museum without the usual crowd, in the glow of moonlight.

As night fell, they entered the quiet, dimly-lit museum. The statues seemed to come alive in the faint light, and each exhibit felt like a new world. John felt like an explorer, discovering secrets of the past.

In the Egyptian section, John stood before a massive stone pyramid. A sign read, "The pyramid holds tales of kings and queens." John closed his eyes, and he imagined he could hear the whispers of ancient pharaohs.

Next, they stepped into the world of dinosaurs. The enormous bones of a T-Rex towered over John. "I bet he roared louder than thunder!" John whispered, and in his mind, he heard the mighty roar echoing in prehistoric forests.

Later, in a room full of shimmering gemstones, John found a small, peculiar rock. "This," said his dad, "is a meteorite—a rock from space!" John's eyes widened in wonder. He imagined the meteorite's long journey across the universe, from a distant star to his very hand.

After hours of adventure, they laid their sleeping bags in the planetarium. Above them, stars and planets moved across the dome. "Every star," whispered John's dad, "has its own story, waiting to be told."

As John drifted to sleep beneath the swirling galaxies, he felt a deep connection to the stories around him. He realized that even though he lived in a small town, there was a vast universe of tales waiting to be discovered.

When dawn broke, John left the museum with a new understanding. Every person, every place, every thing has a story, and all you need is a curious heart to discover them.

Chapter 6.
Noah and the Wish-Granting Stone

In a little house on the edge of a lively town lived Noah, a young boy with a heart full of dreams. Noah was known for his kindness and his never-ending curiosity.

One day, while playing in his backyard, Noah spotted something shiny among the flowers. It was a beautiful, sparkling stone. Intrigued, he picked it up and decided to show it to his grandmother, who knew all about mysterious and magical things.

With eyes wide open, Grandma listened as Noah excitedly told her how he'd found the stone. She smiled gently and said, "Noah, my dear, this looks like a very special wish-granting stone. But remember, it can grant only one wish, so choose wisely."

Noah's eyes sparkled with excitement. A wish-granting stone! The possibilities were endless. He could wish for a mountain of toys, endless candy, or maybe even to be a superhero!

But as Noah thought about it more, he remembered his friend Timmy, who had been feeling sad lately because his family couldn't afford a new wheelchair for him. Timmy loved to play basketball, but his old wheelchair made it difficult.

That night, Noah lay in bed, the sparkling stone clenched in his hand. He realized that making Timmy happy was more important than any toy or candy. With all his heart, he whispered his wish into the night: "I wish for a new wheelchair for Timmy, so he can play basketball with us."

The next morning, a brand new wheelchair was delivered to Timmy's house. Nobody knew where it came from, but Noah had a warm feeling in his heart. He knew he had made the right choice.

When Noah told Grandma what he had wished for, she hugged him tightly. "Noah, you used your one wish to bring joy to someone else. That, my dear, is the greatest wish of all."

Timmy was overjoyed with his new wheelchair, and he played basketball like a champ. And though Noah's wish-granting stone had lost its sparkle, Noah had gained something much more valuable—the joy of giving and the knowledge that the best wishes are those that bring happiness to everyone.

Chapter 7.
Samuel's Whispering Palms

In a cozy little house surrounded by a bustling city, lived a bright-eyed boy named Samuel. Samuel had a curious soul and a heart full of wonder. He loved to explore, ask questions, and dream of faraway places.

Every night, he would close his eyes and embark on fantastical adventures in his dreams.

One magical night, Samuel found himself in a land like no other; a dense, green forest filled with tall, slender palm trees. As he wandered through this enchanting world, he felt the gentle breeze rustling the leaves. But wait! It wasn't just the wind. The trees... they were whispering!

"Hello there, young traveler," said one tall palm tree, bending down to greet Samuel.

Samuel's eyes widened in surprise. "You can talk?" he gasped.

"Indeed, we can," chuckled another tree. "In this land, we trees have been given the gift of speech."

Samuel was eager to learn more. "What can you tell me about this beautiful forest?"

The palm trees swayed gracefully, their leaves shimmering. "This is a place where every creature, every plant, has a purpose," said the first tree. "We trees give shade and homes to animals, provide fruits, and even help make the air clean."

"But," sighed the second tree, "not everyone understands the value of nature. Some come to our forest and harm it, cutting down our friends and leaving trash behind."

Samuel felt a pang in his heart. "That's so sad. Why would anyone do that?"

The trees whispered among themselves, and then one of them said, "Many don't realize that nature is full of magic and wisdom. If they did, they would cherish it more."

Samuel listened intently. The palm trees shared tales of ancient times, of nature's wonders, and of the peaceful balance that should exist between humans and the Earth.

As the sun began to rise, Samuel felt his dream coming to an end. But before he woke up, the tallest palm tree leaned down and whispered, "Remember, young one, nature is a precious gift. Cherish it, protect it, and share its magic with others."

When Samuel opened his eyes, he was back in his room. But the words of the whispering palms stayed with him. He became a little guardian of nature, reminding his friends and family about the importance of caring for the Earth and respecting all its creatures.

Nature holds a special magic that deserves our respect and protection. When we take the time to listen and understand, we can be guardians of the Earth and share its wonders with generations to come.

Chapter 8.
Oliver's Secret Superpower

In a bustling little town filled with laughter and play, lived a six-year-old boy named Oliver with a heart as wide as the ocean. Oliver had a special talent, a unique superpower that set him apart from other kids his age—he had the remarkable ability to sense and understand the feelings of those around him.

One sunny day, Oliver and his classmates went on a school trip to the zoo. Oliver was brimming with excitement, eagerly awaiting the adventures of the day.

As they walked through the zoo, marveling at the lions, elephants, and monkeys, Oliver noticed his friend, Hannah, standing quietly by the penguin enclosure, her face fallen and her eyes filled with tears.

Oliver's heart reached out to her, and without a moment's hesitation, he approached Hannah, his voice gentle. "Hey, Hannah, what's wrong? Why are you sad?"

Hannah looked up, her tears making her eyes glisten. "I dropped my favorite toy

penguin somewhere. I can't find it, and now it's all alone," she sniffled.

Oliver could feel the sadness and loss that Hannah was experiencing. It was as if her emotions were flowing into him, and he could understand her pain. He knew he had to help.

"Don't worry, Hannah. Let's retrace your steps and find your penguin together. I'm sure it's waiting for you," Oliver said with a reassuring smile.

With renewed hope, Hannah nodded, and together they searched the zoo. Oliver kept talking to Hannah as they searched, sharing stories of times he had lost something important and how he had felt. Hannah felt understood, and not so alone in her sadness.

Finally, after looking for what felt like an adventure in itself, they found the toy penguin hidden behind a bench, just waiting to be found.

"Here it is, Hannah! Your penguin was just playing hide and seek!" Oliver exclaimed, his heart swelling with joy as he saw the happiness light up Hannah's face.

Hannah hugged her toy tightly, a big smile replacing her tears. "Thank you, Oliver! You're the best!"

Oliver felt a warm glow inside, knowing he had made a difference. "Anytime, Hannah. That's what friends are for!"

As the day ended and the bus rolled back towards their school, Oliver realized something important. His ability to understand and feel what others were feeling was something truly special. It allowed him to connect, help, and spread kindness wherever he went.

And as the sun set, painting the sky in hues of pink and orange, Oliver knew that being Captain Empathy was the best superpower anyone could have.

Chapter 9.
Soccer Dreams

In a sunny town, where kids loved to play outdoors, lived a boy named Liam. Liam had curly brown hair, never-ending energy, and one big dream: to be the best soccer player in town!

Every day after school, Liam would rush to the playground with his soccer ball. He would practice dribbling, shooting, and even some fancy footwork he'd seen on TV. But there was a problem. Every time Liam played in a real game with his friends, he'd get nervous and miss his shots. His feet felt like they were tied in knots, and the ball never seemed to go where he wanted.

A kind old man named Mr. Garcia would always sit on the park bench watching the kids play. One day, after another missed goal, Mr. Garcia called Liam over.

"Why so glum, young man?" Mr. Garcia asked, his eyes twinkling.

"I just want to score a goal and make my team proud. But I always mess up," Liam replied, looking down.

Mr. Garcia smiled. "You know, Liam, soccer isn't just about scoring goals. It's about having fun, teamwork, and always doing your best."

"But I practice so much, and I still can't get it right!" Liam exclaimed.

The old man chuckled. "When I was young, I wanted to be a dancer. I practiced every day, just like you. But I always tripped during the big performances. One day, I realized I was so worried about making mistakes that I forgot to enjoy dancing!"

Liam looked up, curious. "So what did you do?"

"I danced for fun, not for perfection. And guess what? When I enjoyed myself, I danced better!" Mr. Garcia said with a wink.

Inspired, Liam decided to change his approach. The next time he played, he focused on enjoying the game, passing the ball to his friends, and cheering even when they missed. And then, without even thinking about it, Liam saw an opportunity, took a shot, and scored his first goal!

The whole playground erupted in cheers. Liam's friends rushed over to him, patting his back and lifting him in the air. But Liam realized something even more important than the goal he had scored. He had learned to enjoy the journey, the play, and the shared moments with his friends.

That evening, as the sun painted the sky in golden shades, Liam sat next to Mr. Garcia, sharing his victory. The old man smiled. "Remember, Liam, it's not always about winning or being the best. It's about enjoying what you do and sharing those moments with others."

Liam nodded, his heart full of gratitude and joy. With a determined spirit and a newfound love for the game, Liam would go on to do great things. His soccer dreams were only just beginning.

Chapter 10.
Tiny Defender

In the little town of Green Meadows, kids from all over would gather at the central playground. It had the highest slides, the most swings, and a giant sandbox in the middle. But there was one more thing

special about this playground: Jamie, the Tiny Defender.

Jamie was the smallest boy in his class. Some of his shoes even had a little extra padding just so they would fit! But what Jamie lacked in size, he made up in courage and determination.

One sunny day, while Jamie was building a sandcastle in the sandbox, he noticed a big boy named Rex taking toys from the younger kids. Rex was known for being a bit of a bully, and today he had set his sights on little Lily's toy shovel.

Jamie stood up to confront him, but Rex just laughed. "You're too small to stop me."

But Jamie, with a deep breath and a steady voice, said, "It's not about how big you are,

but how big your heart is. Give Lily back her shovel."

Rex was surprised. No one had ever stood up to him like that, especially not the smallest boy in the playground. The other kids gathered around, watching to see what would happen next.

Instead of using his fists, Jamie used his words. "This playground is for everyone to share and have fun. If you're feeling sad or left out, there are better ways to ask for help or make friends."

Rex looked around, seeing the eyes of all the other children on him. At that moment, he felt really small. He handed the shovel back to Lily. "I... I just wanted to build something too," he mumbled.

Jamie smiled. "Well, why didn't you say so? Come join us! We can build a bigger castle together."

And just like that, the playground transformed. Everyone, including Rex, worked together. The castle they built was the grandest Green Meadows had ever seen. And at the top, flying high, was a flag that read: "Tiny Defender's Castle."

From that day on, Jamie wasn't just known for being the smallest. He was known for his big heart, bravery, and the ability to bring everyone together.

Chapter 11.
Courage at the Creek

In the charming town of Willowbrook,
beyond the green hills and shimmering
meadows, lay a winding creek. It was filled
with smooth stones and darting fish, and
echoed the songs of chirping birds. All the

children loved playing there, but they were all careful not to go too deep, for there was a part of the creek that everyone called the 'Whispering Waters.'

Legend said that the Whispering Waters was where the creek got deep and the waters rushed faster. The older kids dared each other to cross it, but most kept away, including a young boy named Jake.

Jake was known for his adventurous spirit. He had climbed the tallest trees and explored the darkest corners of the woods. But the Whispering Waters? That was one challenge he hadn't tried yet.

One day, Jake was playing near the creek with his little sister, Emma. Emma had brought Mr. Hops with her, a stuffed bunny who was her favorite toy. They were playing

chase along the water's edge when, suddenly, Mr. Hops fell out of Emma's hands and into the creek!

"Mr. Hops!" Emma cried, her eyes filling with tears as she saw her beloved toy drifting towards the Whispering Waters.

Without thinking twice, Jake's protective instincts kicked in. But instead of jumping recklessly into the water, he paused and took a deep breath. There had to be a safer way of rescuing Mr. Hops. Then he remembered the bridge made of stepping stones that led across the creek. It was a tricky path, especially near the Whispering Waters, but he felt it was the safest choice.

The other children in Willowbrook gathered to watch as Jake rushed towards the stepping stones. Step by careful step,

Jake made his way across the creek, each stone feeling more wobbly than the last. The water rushed around him, making his heart race. But with each step, he remembered Emma's hopeful eyes and Mr. Hops, now just within his reach.

With one final leap, Jake managed to grab Mr. Hops, avoiding the deepest part of the Whispering Waters. Cheers erupted from the other children, and a relieved Emma ran towards her brother, hugging both him and her rescued toy.

Jake felt a warmth in his chest. It wasn't the thrill of crossing the Whispering Waters that made him happy—it was the joy of helping someone he loved.

That evening, as the stars sparkled above Willowbrook, Jake and Emma sat by their

window, Mr. Hops safely tucked in between them.

Jake whispered, "Sometimes courage isn't just about facing the big challenges, but knowing the best way to face them."

Cuddling Mr. Hops, Emma replied, "And sometimes, courage is having a big brother like you."

Chapter 12.
You are Loved

In a warm and cozy house, lived a little boy named Henry. Henry had sparkling blue eyes, a contagious giggle, and a heart full of love. But sometimes, Henry felt a little bit sad and lonely.

Henry's parents worked a lot, and even though they spent as much time as they could with him, Henry wished they could be around more. He often played with his toy cars and built tall towers with his blocks, but it wasn't as fun without someone to share it with.

One day, Henry's grandma came to visit. She had a twinkle in her eye and a smile that could light up any room. She noticed Henry sitting by himself, looking a bit down.

"What's the matter, my little sunshine?" Grandma asked, sitting next to him.

"I just wish Mommy and Daddy could play with me more," Henry mumbled, kicking his feet.

Grandma gave him a big hug. "Oh, Henry. Your mommy and daddy love you more than anything in the world. They work hard to make sure you have everything you need."

"But I miss them, Grandma," Henry said, his eyes starting to well up.

"I know, sweetheart. But you are always in their hearts, and they are always in yours. Love doesn't go away just because we're not together," Grandma explained, wiping away a small tear from Henry's cheek.

To show him, Grandma took out a small, heart-shaped locket from her pocket. "This was given to me by your grandpa. Even when he was far away, I could look at this locket and feel his love."

Henry looked at the locket, his eyes wide with wonder.

"Now, how about we make a love box for you?" Grandma suggested with a smile.

"A love box?" Henry asked, curious.

"Yes! Every time Mommy and Daddy have to go to work, they can leave a little note or a small surprise for you in the box. And you can put something for them in too. This way, you all can feel each other's love, no matter where you are!"

Henry's face lit up. "That sounds fun, Grandma!"

So, they spent the afternoon decorating a small box with glitter, stickers, and lots of love. Henry even wrote the first note to put inside: "I love you, Mommy and Daddy."

When Henry's parents came home, they were touched by the love box idea. From that day on, they never forgot to leave a little something for Henry, and he did the same for them.

Henry realized that even when he was alone, he was never really alone. He was surrounded by love, and that made all the difference.

Chapter 13.
Pet friends

Once upon a sunny day, in a small, cozy house, lived a six-year-old boy named Tommy and his fluffy cat, Whiskers. Tommy and Whiskers were the best of friends. They played together, laughed together, and shared all their secrets.

One day, while they were playing in the backyard, a little bird fell out of its nest. The bird was shivering with fear. Tommy saw the bird and his heart filled with kindness.

"Whiskers, we have to help!" Tommy said, looking at his furry friend.

Whiskers, with his big, green eyes, meowed as if he understood. Tommy carefully picked up the little bird and said, "Don't worry, little birdie. We will take care of you." They named the bird Sky.

Tommy and Whiskers worked together to make a soft bed of leaves for Sky. They gave him some water and found some seeds for him to eat. Slowly, the little bird started to feel better.

Every day, Tommy and Whiskers would visit Sky, making sure he was safe and happy. They talked to him, sang songs, and even told him stories. And every day, Sky grew stronger and happier.

Tommy and Whiskers loved playing with Sky, but they also knew that once his wing was healed, it was essential to let Sky fly and be free.

One evening, as Tommy was telling Sky about his day, he whispered, "You know, Sky, I wish you could stay with me forever, but I also want you to fly high and free."

Sky chirped as if he understood. The next morning, Tommy and Whiskers found that Sky's wing had healed completely. They knew it was time.

With a heavy heart, Tommy took the box outside and opened it. Sky fluttered his wings, looked at Tommy and Whiskers for a moment, and then soared high up in the sky.

That evening, as Tommy and Whiskers were sitting in the backyard, they noticed something amazing. A group of birds flew down, all chirping happily, with Sky leading them. It seemed as though Sky had brought his friends to meet Tommy.

Every day after that, the birds would visit Tommy and Whiskers and play with them. Though Sky was free to roam the skies, he never forgot the boy who had once cared for him. And Tommy learned an important lesson: true friends always come back to you, no matter where they go.

Tommy discovered true friendship is about understanding, caring, and letting go when needed. And sometimes, the best friends might not be humans, but pets who love you unconditionally.

Chapter 14.
Braving the Shadows

Once upon a time, in a small, sunny town, lived a little boy named Jack. Jack was six years old and full of energy and curiosity. He loved to explore, play, and learn new things. But there was one thing that Jack was really scared of—the dark.

Every night, when the lights went out, Jack would pull his covers up to his chin and squeeze his eyes shut, trying to keep the darkness away. He had a small nightlight, but it didn't seem to help much. Jack was afraid that there might be monsters hiding in the shadows, waiting to jump out and scare him.

One evening, Jack's mom noticed that he seemed more scared than usual. She sat down on the edge of his bed and asked, "Jack, what's wrong? You seem really upset tonight."

Jack looked up at his mom with wide, fearful eyes and whispered, "Mom, I'm

really scared of the dark. I think there might be monsters in my room."

Jack's mom smiled gently and said, "Oh, Jack, I promise you there are no monsters in your room. But I understand that the dark can be scary. Do you want to talk about it?"

Jack nodded and, with his mom's encouragement, he began to share all of his fears about the dark and the monsters he imagined were hiding there. As he talked, Jack realized that saying his fears out loud made them seem less scary.

His mom listened carefully and then said, "Jack, it's okay to be scared. Everyone feels scared sometimes. But you know what? Fears are there to overcome. When we face our fears, we often learn that they're not as scary as we thought."

Jack looked up at his mom, curiosity shining in his eyes. "But how do I face the dark, Mom?"

His mom thought for a moment and then said, "How about we start by leaving the nightlight off tonight, and I'll stay with you until you fall asleep. We can face the dark together."

Jack was nervous, but he trusted his mom. So, with a deep breath, he agreed to try it. That night, with his mom by his side, Jack faced the dark. And you know what? It wasn't as scary as he'd thought. Jack realized that the dark was just the absence of light, and there were no monsters hiding in the shadows.

From that night on, Jack wasn't afraid of the dark anymore. He learned that his mom was

right, fears are there to overcome, and that when he faced his fears, he found courage and strength he didn't know he had.

And so, dear reader, remember Jack's story and know that it's okay to be scared. But also remember that fears are there to overcome, and when you face your fears, you can find courage, strength, and maybe even a little bit of magic.

Conclusion

Dear boy,

Wow, what an amazing adventure we've had together! We've laughed, learned, and grown through each and every story. I hope you've enjoyed them as much as I have enjoyed sharing them with you.

These tales were filled with brave boys, big dreams, and lots of courage. Remember, just like the characters in our stories, you have a strong heart and a brilliant mind. You can achieve anything you set your mind to!

Dreaming big is the first step to doing big things. Never stop imagining, creating, and believing in yourself. Your ideas are special, and your courage is powerful. You can be a hero in your own story, just by being you.

And don't forget, being brave doesn't mean you're never scared. It means you try, even when things are tough. You have a strong spirit and a loving heart, and that makes you fantastic!

As we close our book, I want to remind you that every day is a new chapter, filled with chances to learn and grow. Keep dreaming big, dear boy, and always believe in the fantastic person you are.

Thank you for sharing this journey with me. Here's to many more stories, adventures, and dreams!

Dear Parent who reads this book,

We hope you enjoyed the stories in it and the time spent discussing the valuable lessons they teach with your child.

For adults only ☺ we have prepared **a special guide that outlines 12 key concepts** with actionable ideas **to foster self-esteem and self-confidence in children.**

You can download, print, and put these ideas into practice regularly and integrate the proposed exercises into your child´s routine.

Get your guide here ↓

If you enjoyed this book, we encourage you to leave a review on its Amazon page so other parents can benefit from it as well